Hercules and the Stables

retold by Rebecca Grudzina • illustrated by Bill Greenhead

3

Hercules was a very strong man.
He lived near a king.

The king had many cows.
Hercules wanted some cows.

The cows lived in big stables.
The stables were very dirty.
They were too big to clean.

6

"I want some cows," Hercules told the king.

8

"Then clean the stables in one day. I will give you cows," the king said.

Hercules made a hole.

He made another hole.

He dug a path to the river.

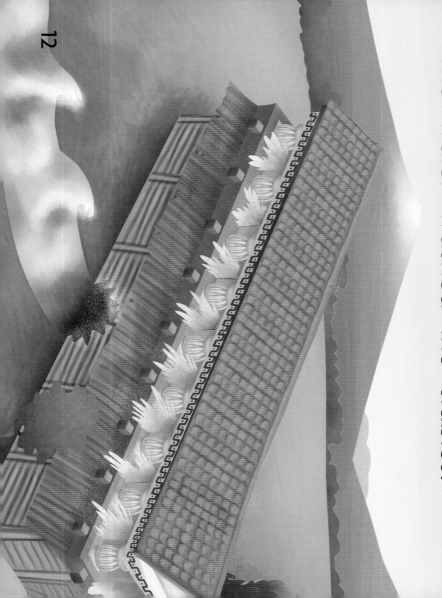

The water came down the path.
The water washed the stables.

13

The stables were clean, but the king wanted to keep his cows.

"I did not say
I would give you cows!"
the king said.

His son said,
"Yes, you did!
I heard you!"

And so the king gave Hercules some cows.